MISSION
TO
MARS

CAN YOU SURVIVE IN SPACE?

MISSION TO MARS

CAN YOU SURVIVE IN SPACE?

Written by Dr Sheila Kanani

Illustrated by Adamastor

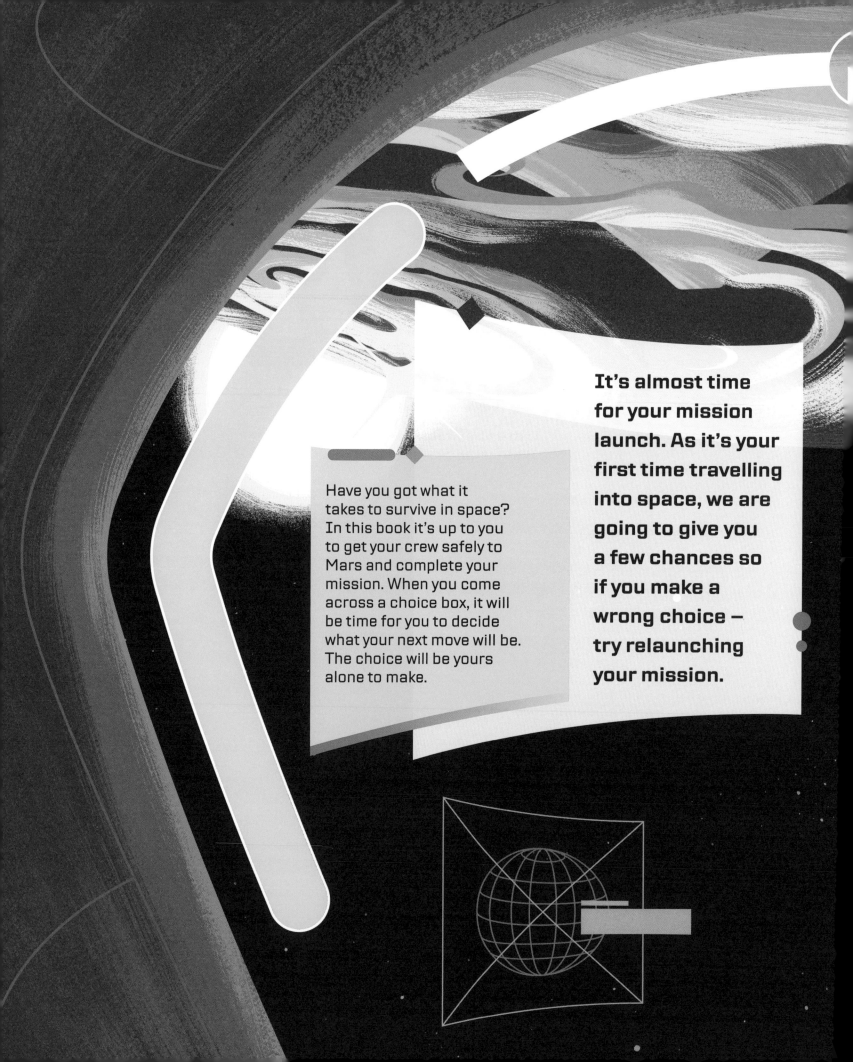

Have you got what it takes to survive in space? In this book it's up to you to get your crew safely to Mars and complete your mission. When you come across a choice box, it will be time for you to decide what your next move will be. The choice will be yours alone to make.

It's almost time for your mission launch. As it's your first time travelling into space, we are going to give you a few chances so if you make a wrong choice – try relaunching your mission.

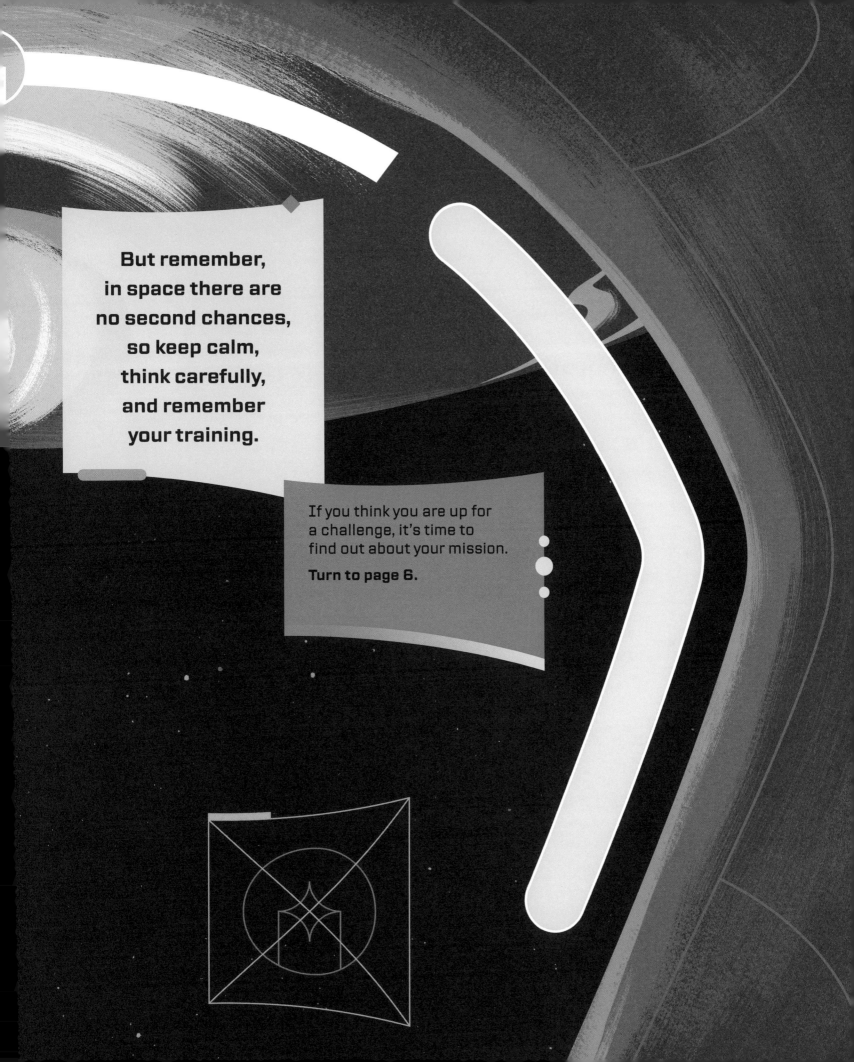

But remember,
in space there are
no second chances,
so keep calm,
think carefully,
and remember
your training.

If you think you are up for
a challenge, it's time to
find out about your mission.

Turn to page 6.

Mission to Mars

Congratulations

You have been selected to be one of the crew for the first-ever human mission to Mars. You showed particular aptitude during the selection process and completed the astronaut training successfully.

If you are triumphant on your mission, you will be the first Earthling to set foot on Mars. But your journey will not be without decisions, danger and distress! It will be up to you to get your crew to Mars safely. Today, we know Mars to be dry and cold, but in the past, there is evidence to suggest there were rivers, lakes and streams! That would mean that Mars was warmer and wetter, so maybe it could have supported life. Once you get there, you will be required to collect rock samples and test for evidence of ancient life on the Red Planet.

TRAINING LOG

Mars has been selected due to its proximity to Earth, but also because it is of scientific interest. The Red Planet might once have been home to liquid water, meaning there is a high possibility that it once harboured life. Mars can be found in the 'Goldilocks Zone' of our Solar System, meaning it is not too hot, not too cold, and just the right distance from the Sun that it could be a potentially habitable place.

Godilocks Zone

Meet the Crew

It takes an extraordinary person to be an astronaut, especially one who can make it to Mars. To complete our mission, we are going to need a stellar crew that excel in all sorts of areas of science, from engineering to medicine. Astronaut training is rigorous and relentless, so we've pulled together the best of the best. Let's meet the crew...

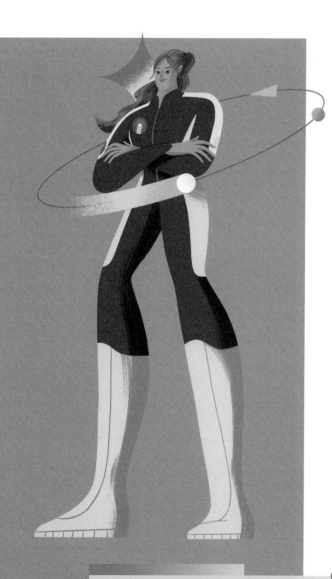

PROJECT ENGINEER

The project engineer is in charge of all the tech on board, from electrical systems to robots! They oversee the operation of rovers, maintain mission software and provide support for any tools that are critical in carrying out the mission. If anything goes wrong, it's up to them to fix it.

CREW DOCTOR

It is the crew doctor's job to make sure that all the other astronauts overcome any health challenges during the mission. There's lots to think about – from the effect of microgravity, homesickness and radiation from space. Who knows, they may even need to use their medical knowledge to treat any life forms found on Mars!

MISSION COMMANDER

The mission commander leads the crew and makes many of the decisions. They need to be very experienced and have worked in the space industry for a long time. They are responsible for any communication between this mission initiated by the European Space Agency and other space agencies.

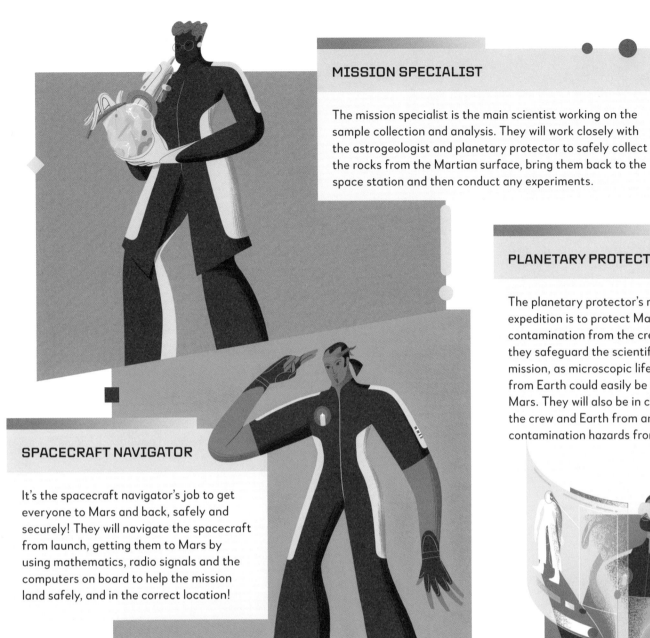

MISSION SPECIALIST

The mission specialist is the main scientist working on the sample collection and analysis. They will work closely with the astrogeologist and planetary protector to safely collect the rocks from the Martian surface, bring them back to the space station and then conduct any experiments.

PLANETARY PROTECTOR

The planetary protector's role in this expedition is to protect Mars from any contamination from the crew. By doing this, they safeguard the scientific goals of the mission, as microscopic life forms brought from Earth could easily be mistaken for life on Mars. They will also be in charge of protecting the crew and Earth from any possible contamination hazards from Mars.

SPACECRAFT NAVIGATOR

It's the spacecraft navigator's job to get everyone to Mars and back, safely and securely! They will navigate the spacecraft from launch, getting them to Mars by using mathematics, radio signals and the computers on board to help the mission land safely, and in the correct location!

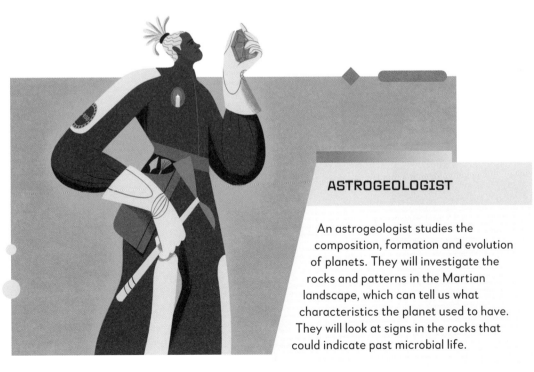

ASTROGEOLOGIST

An astrogeologist studies the composition, formation and evolution of planets. They will investigate the rocks and patterns in the Martian landscape, which can tell us what characteristics the planet used to have. They will look at signs in the rocks that could indicate past microbial life.

Explore the Spacecraft

Welcome to your new home!

Not only will this spacecraft safely deliver you to Mars, but it will also serve as your bedroom, living room, science lab, vehicle and escape route if required. This spacecraft will sustain you during space travel, carry your food and water, and give you a safe re-entry following your journey through deep space.

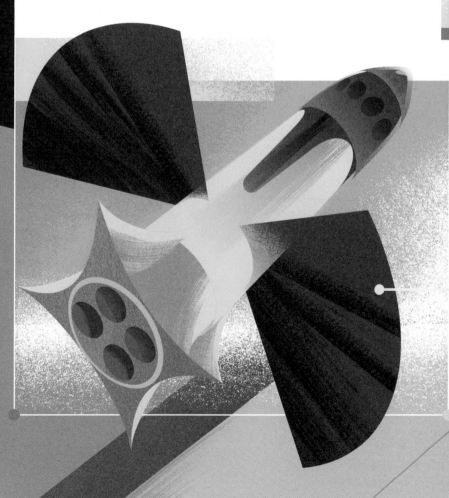

CREW MODULE

You and the rest of the crew will live in the crew module, which is a pressurised capsule where you will live and work during your journey. It is well-equipped, but also small, so let's hope that you get on well with the rest of the crew!

POWER BAYS

Electrical power for your spacecraft is created by solar arrays on wings attached to the spacecraft. 20,000 solar cells change light into electrical energy, providing enough electricity to power three 3-bedroom homes on Earth!

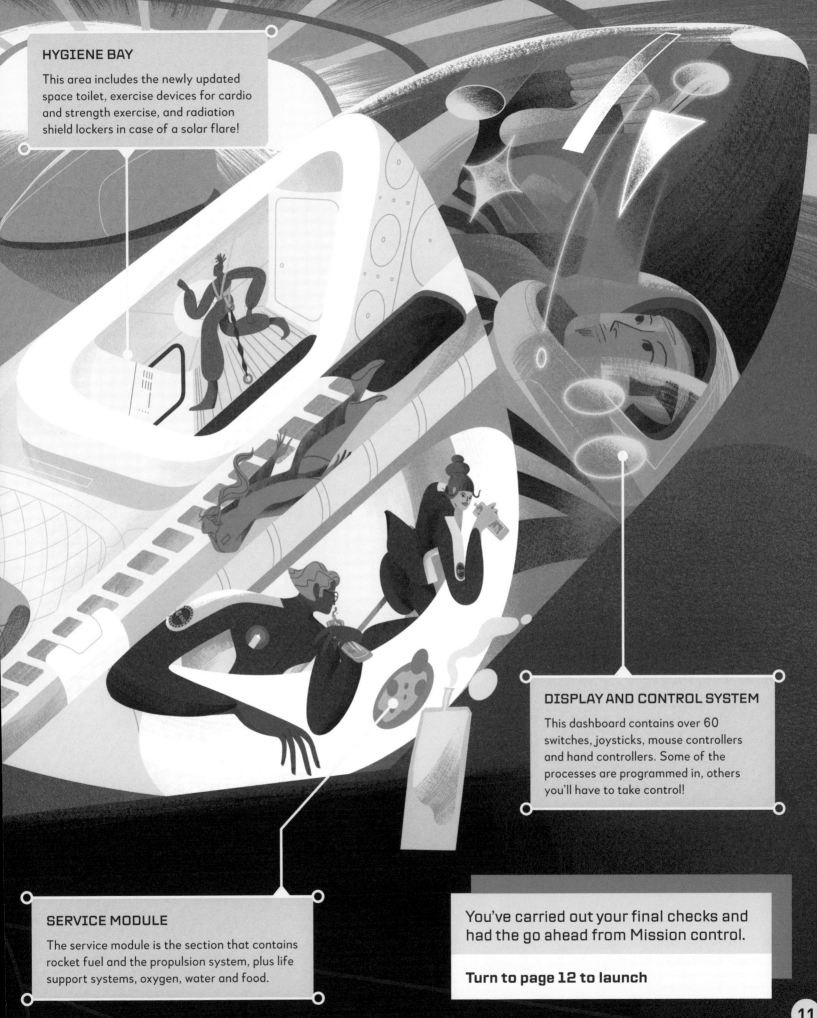

HYGIENE BAY

This area includes the newly updated space toilet, exercise devices for cardio and strength exercise, and radiation shield lockers in case of a solar flare!

DISPLAY AND CONTROL SYSTEM

This dashboard contains over 60 switches, joysticks, mouse controllers and hand controllers. Some of the processes are programmed in, others you'll have to take control!

SERVICE MODULE

The service module is the section that contains rocket fuel and the propulsion system, plus life support systems, oxygen, water and food.

You've carried out your final checks and had the go ahead from Mission control.

Turn to page 12 to launch

T minus ...

3 ...

2 ...

1 ...

...LIFT OFF!

To enter orbit.

Turn to page 14

Orbit

The spacecraft soars gently into the vastness of space, as the sky turns from light blue to darkest black. With the success of the launch, it isn't long before you reach the designated distance from Earth, where you can use the Earth's gravitational pull and start to orbit. The motion of the spacecraft around the Earth comes from two forces: the first is the momentum from launch, pulling the spacecraft in one direction; the second is Earth's gravity which pulls the spacecraft downwards. The balance between these two forces keeps the spacecraft orbiting around the Earth. The crew can use this time to reconfigure the spacecraft and carry out any necessary checks to prepare for deep space travel.

Earth's Orbit

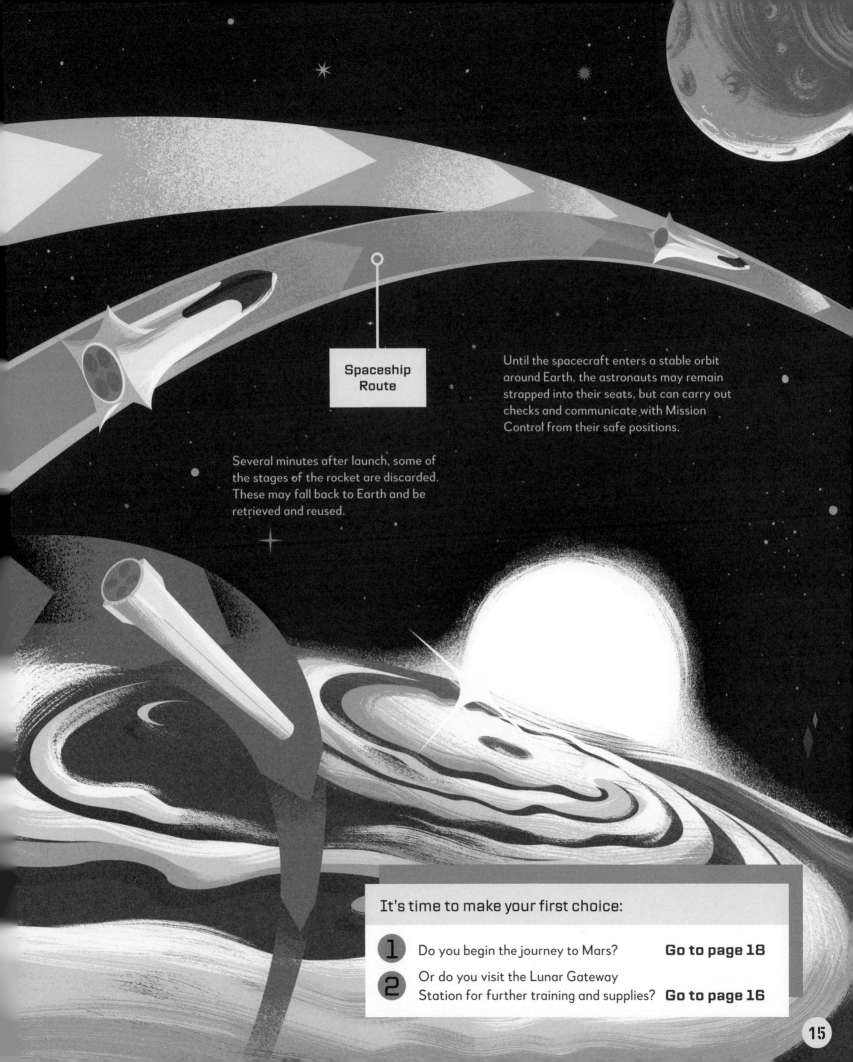

Spaceship Route

Until the spacecraft enters a stable orbit around Earth, the astronauts may remain strapped into their seats, but can carry out checks and communicate with Mission Control from their safe positions.

Several minutes after launch, some of the stages of the rocket are discarded. These may fall back to Earth and be retrieved and reused.

It's time to make your first choice:

1 Do you begin the journey to Mars? **Go to page 18**

2 Or do you visit the Lunar Gateway Station for further training and supplies? **Go to page 16**

Lunar Gateway Station

The Lunar Gateway Station is the Earth's first space station orbiting the Moon and was built by a global team of humans. It provides support to those travelling to the Moon, can be used as a base for scientific experiments as well as act as a stepping stone for deep space exploration.

Your crew have decided to split up your journey and make a stop-off at the Lunar Gateway before your journey to Mars. This gives the crew a chance to finish additional training and stock up on supplies.

The Lunar Gateway is made up of many sections including the orbiter and the lander. **The lander** will allow astronauts to discover the surface of the Moon first-hand, like a shuttle bus between the Moon and the orbiter. The lunar lander is cleverly designed to be able to navigate the difficult conditions on the surface, including no atmosphere and extreme temperatures!

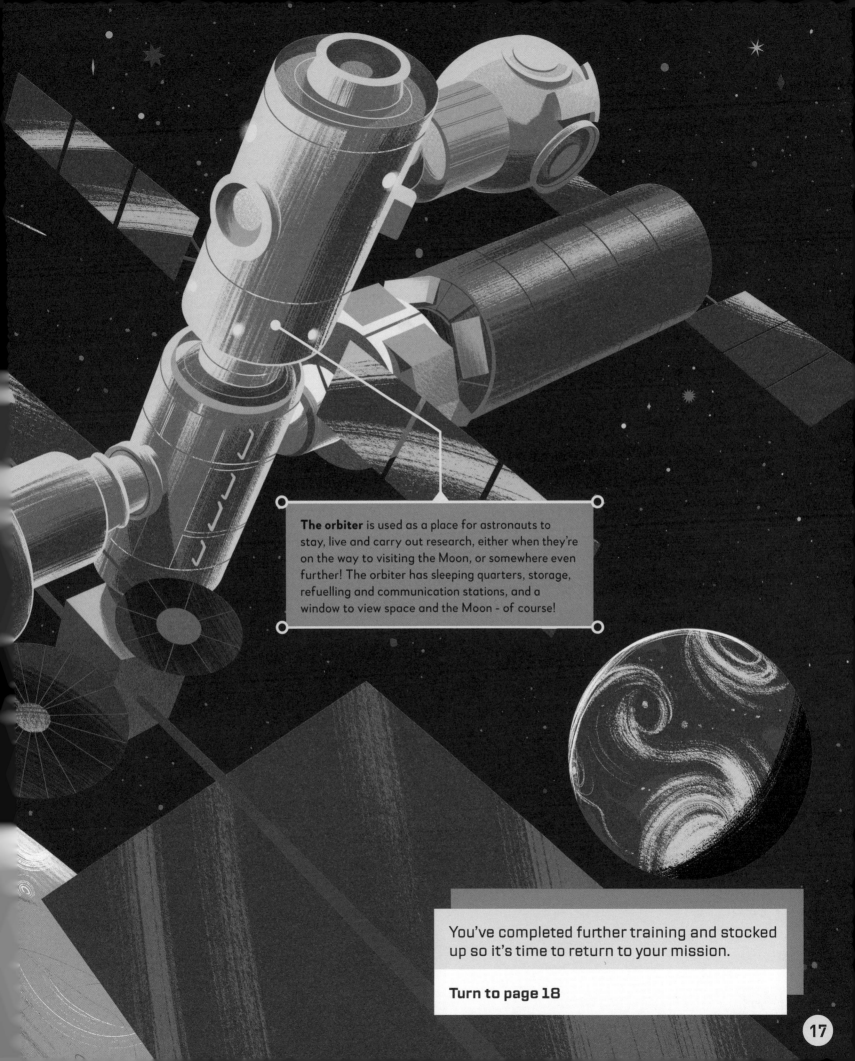

The orbiter is used as a place for astronauts to stay, live and carry out research, either when they're on the way to visiting the Moon, or somewhere even further! The orbiter has sleeping quarters, storage, refuelling and communication stations, and a window to view space and the Moon - of course!

You've completed further training and stocked up so it's time to return to your mission.

Turn to page 18

9 Months Later...

To approach Mars.

Turn to page 20

Docking

You are now approaching the Mars Gateway Station and soon you will be docking. The station will be your home for the duration of your mission. The orbital section of your plan is essential, splitting your mission into two sections. The orbital part of the mission on the MGS allows you to carry out research and some exploration of Mars while orbiting around the Red Planet. From this vantage point you can also develop a deeper knowledge about Mars' moons – Phobos and Deimos.

Mars
Gateway
Station

TRAINING LOG

Phobos and Deimos are smaller than Earth's Moon, with Phobos, the larger moon, orbiting closer to Mars.

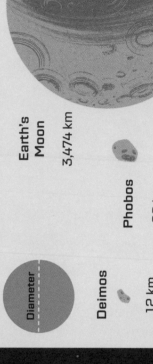

Diameter

Earth's
Moon

3,474 km

Deimos

Phobos

12 km

22 km

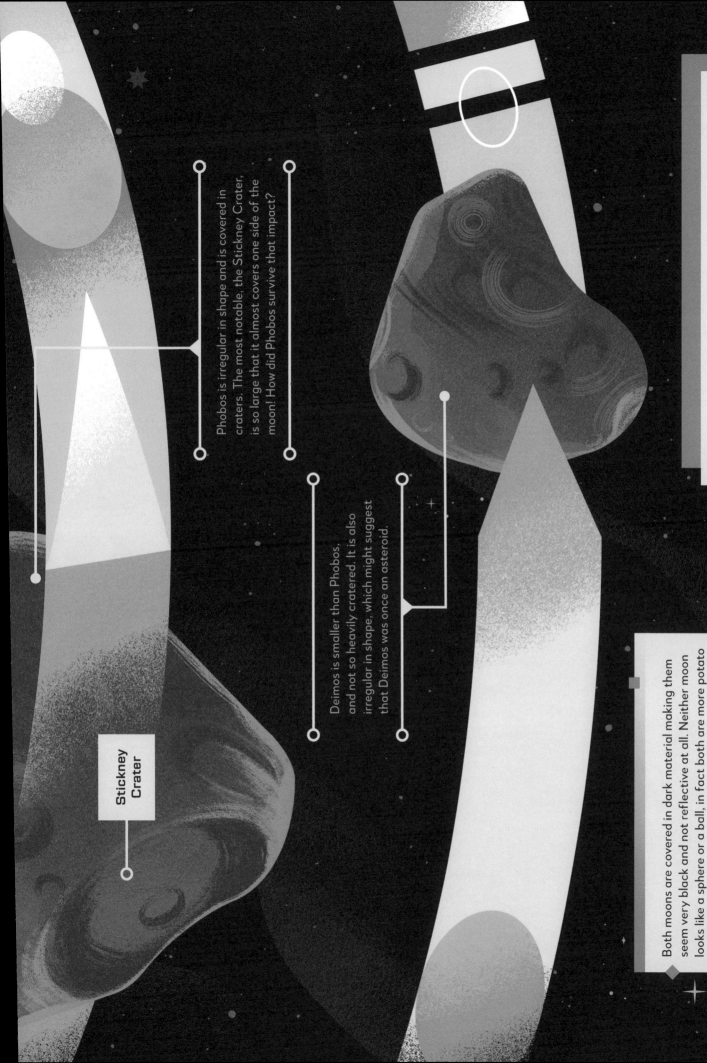

Phobos is irregular in shape and is covered in craters. The most notable, the Stickney Crater, is so large that it almost covers one side of the moon! How did Phobos survive that impact?

Deimos is smaller than Phobos, and not so heavily cratered. It is also irregular in shape, which might suggest that Deimos was once an asteroid.

Stickney Crater

Both moons are covered in dark material making them seem very black and not reflective at all. Neither moon looks like a sphere or a ball, in fact both are more potato shaped! Phobos can feel the tug of Mars' gravity and is likely to smash into Mars in the future. This could create lots of debris that might make a ring around Mars!

Safely onboard the Mars Gateway Station, it's time to prepare for the next stage of your mission.

Turn to page 22

Prepare for Landing

It is time to get ready to land on the Red Planet! It isn't going to be easy! Everything has to go perfectly for you to land gently on the surface, and in the right place! There are a few good spots to aim for, but we want to end up in a place like the Holden Crater where the landscape suggests there might once have been water. The difficulty is that this terrain is challenging to land on, and the Martian atmosphere is thin so there is less air resistance to slow your descent. There are many hazards to avoid, including steep crater edges, boulders and sediment.

TRAINING LOG

Holden Crater
At 140 km wide, this is a large impact crater, which has evolved in shape due to the strong winds and storms on Mars. These have covered the centre of the crater in sediment. The crater has an 'alluvial fan' shape showing material that has been transported by water and some evidence of rock falls at the edges of the crater.

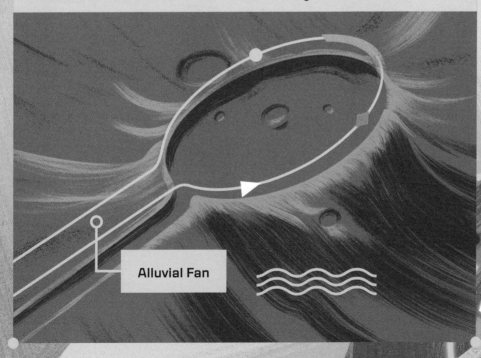

Alluvial Fan

1

If you are the mission specialist, astrogeologist or planetary protector you will be heading down to the surface of Mars! You must work as a team to study the landing site, think about which samples you want to safely collect, and thoroughly investigate the rocks and features in the Martian landscape.

2

Mawrth Vallis

Holden Crater

Margarititer Terra

SW Melas Chasma

You've got two options now.

1   Do you stay on the Mars Gateway Station? **Turn to page 30**

2   Or do you head to the surface of Mars?   **Turn to page 24**

Commence Landing

You've been in space for 9 months by now, and Earth is a pale blue 'star' in the cupola window view. You'll soon be expected to guide the crew through the landing. You are currently hurtling through space at over 21,500 km/h, but it won't be long until you have to manage the EDL! This is **e**ntry, **d**escent and **l**anding on the surface of Mars.

EDL will not be easy. Your crew are depending on your knowledge and precision. The atmosphere of Mars is extremely thin, over 150 times thinner than the Earth's, and is made up of different gases to the Earth's atmosphere. This means it will be much harder to land on Mars due to the lack of drag. Drag is a force that acts in the opposite direction to the motion of the spacecraft and is important in helping your spacecraft slow down!

1

TRAINING LOG

You need to think carefully about how to descend in the best way, so that you carry out each step of the EDL to perfection. One wrong choice and you could veer off course, ending up landing miles away from where you need to be. Big errors might mean you may plummet in an uncontrollable nosedive, landing instead as a wreck on the surface!

EARTH

MARS

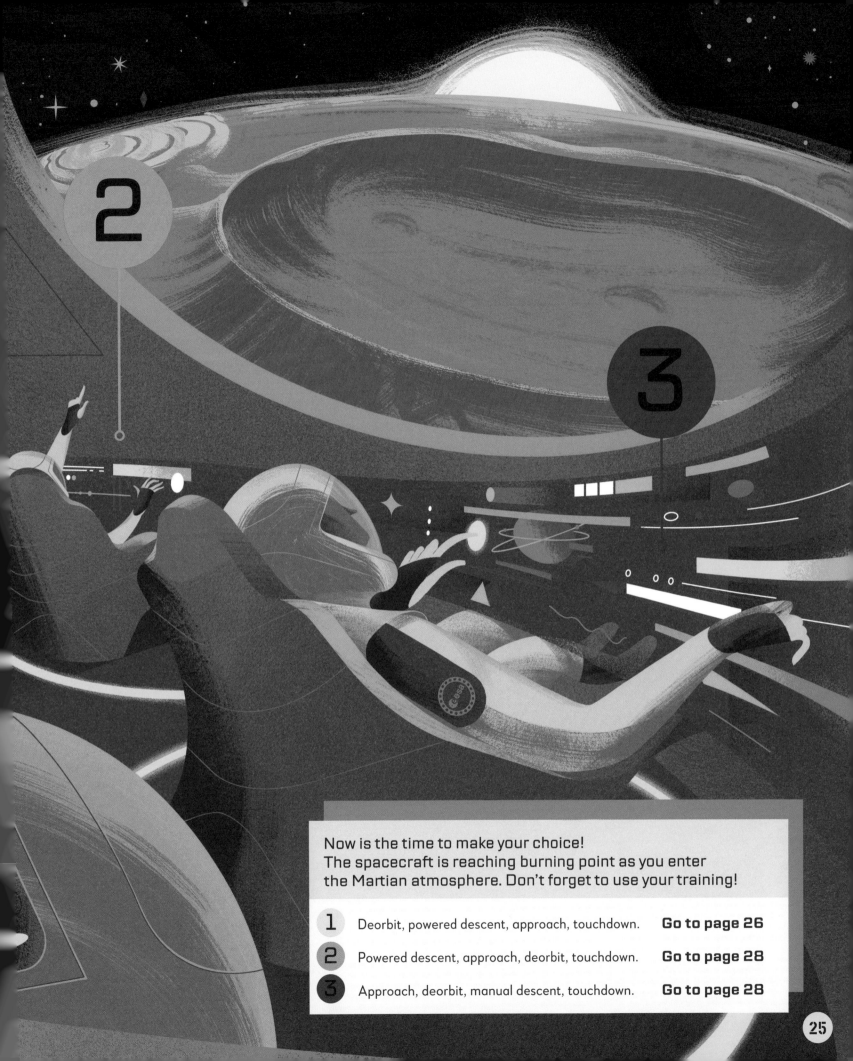

Now is the time to make your choice!
The spacecraft is reaching burning point as you enter
the Martian atmosphere. Don't forget to use your training!

1 Deorbit, powered descent, approach, touchdown. **Go to page 26**

2 Powered descent, approach, deorbit, touchdown. **Go to page 28**

3 Approach, deorbit, manual descent, touchdown. **Go to page 28**

First Person On Mars

Great choice! You've executed the first successful landing of a human spaceflight on Mars – right on track within the Holden Crater. But your landing is not the only important aspect. To survive on Mars and eventually head back to Earth, a number of additional spacecraft containing supplies, fuel and vehicles were due to land with you. However, something must have gone wrong, as they are not at the Holden Crater. You need to find the rest of your supplies, and fast, as your spacecraft only contains enough necessities to last 7 Martian days.

1

2

esa

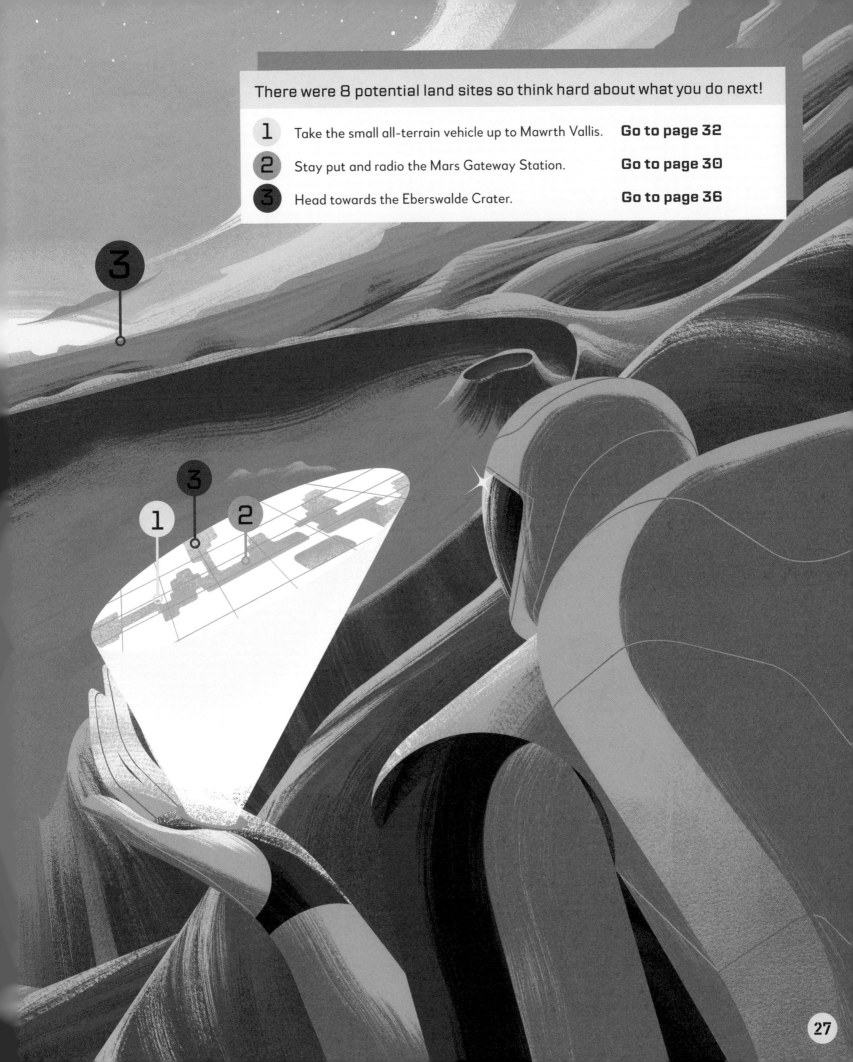

There were 8 potential land sites so think hard about what you do next!

1 Take the small all-terrain vehicle up to Mawrth Vallis. **Go to page 32**

2 Stay put and radio the Mars Gateway Station. **Go to page 30**

3 Head towards the Eberswalde Crater. **Go to page 36**

29%
OXYGEN

○ ○ ○ STA

MISS
FAI

TUS ○ ○ ○

ION
LURE

42%
BATTERY

Surviving in space is tough and
unfortunately, you've made the wrong
choice. But don't give up — why not
relaunch the mission and try again?

Turn to page 14

Meanwhile ... Back on the Station

You're running your regular checks when the comms machine whirrs into action. You call for the mission commander – the surface crew are lost! They have become separated from their supplies. You, and the others who are still on the station, will need to locate the supplies and relay the information to the surface crew, but your time is limited before you lose contact! The surface crew are in the Holden Crater, but where are the supplies? You'll need to locate the missing items and inform the rest of the crew, so that they can travel to the important resources and bring everything back to the base station!

1

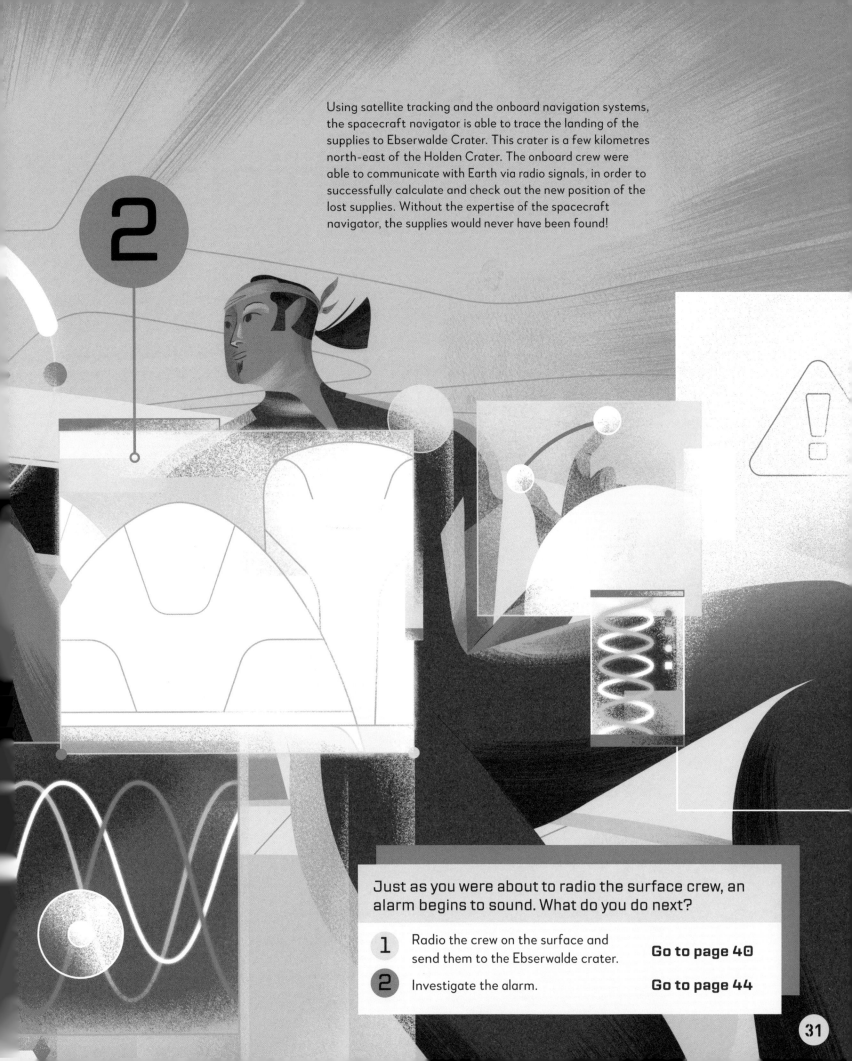

2

Using satellite tracking and the onboard navigation systems, the spacecraft navigator is able to trace the landing of the supplies to Ebserwalde Crater. This crater is a few kilometres north-east of the Holden Crater. The onboard crew were able to communicate with Earth via radio signals, in order to successfully calculate and check out the new position of the lost supplies. Without the expertise of the spacecraft navigator, the supplies would never have been found!

Just as you were about to radio the surface crew, an alarm begins to sound. What do you do next?

1 Radio the crew on the surface and send them to the Ebserwalde crater.

Go to page 40

2 Investigate the alarm.

Go to page 44

Navigating in the All-Terrain Vehicle

You have decided to use the All-Terrain Vehicle to navigate the surface of Mars. Mars is very cold and the surface is covered in red dust. There are rocks, canyons, volcanoes, dried-up river beds and craters. High winds whip up the dust into storms, which can last for months. So, your ATV needs to be able to cope with all the challenges that Mars might throw at you! The dust can ruin the instrumentation on the ATV, scratch it and clog up the mechanisms. And the dust moves fast! Up to 96 km per hour!

TRAINING LOG

The surface of Mars is red due to the presence of iron oxide in the rocks and soil. Iron oxide is created when iron meets oxygen. Iron oxide is commonly known as rust. The iron oxide is present in the dust too – so Mars looks red to us due to the rusty dust!

The ATV is well-equipped to explore Mars.

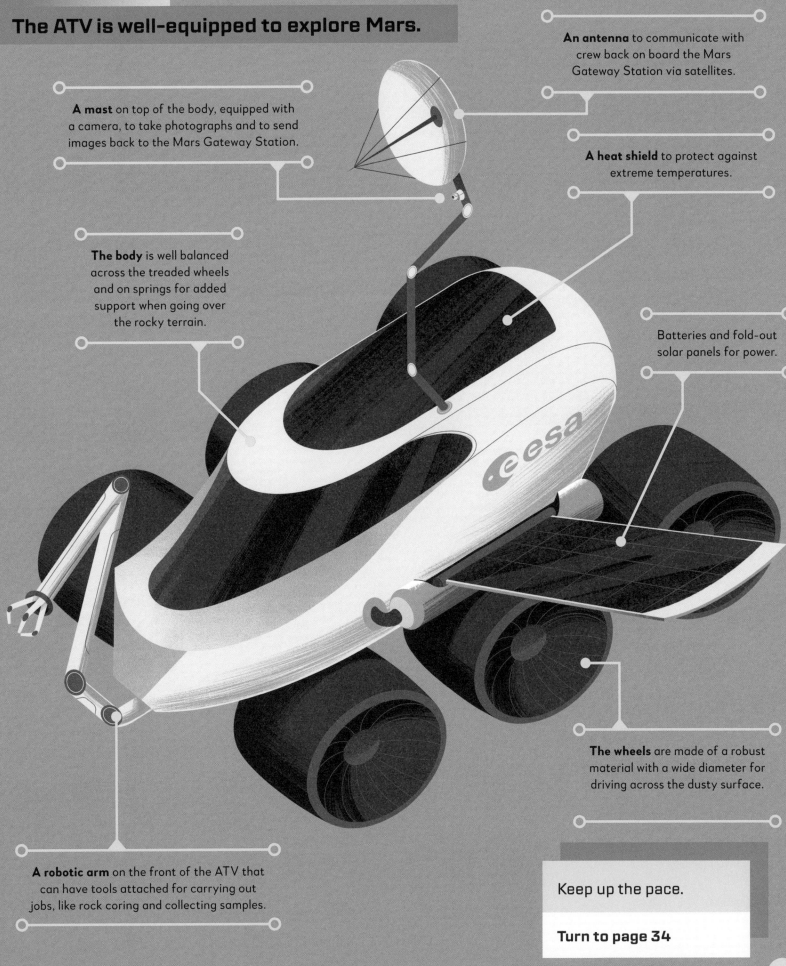

A mast on top of the body, equipped with a camera, to take photographs and to send images back to the Mars Gateway Station.

An antenna to communicate with crew back on board the Mars Gateway Station via satellites.

A heat shield to protect against extreme temperatures.

The body is well balanced across the treaded wheels and on springs for added support when going over the rocky terrain.

Batteries and fold-out solar panels for power.

The wheels are made of a robust material with a wide diameter for driving across the dusty surface.

A robotic arm on the front of the ATV that can have tools attached for carrying out jobs, like rock coring and collecting samples.

Keep up the pace.

Turn to page 34

The Search
Continues

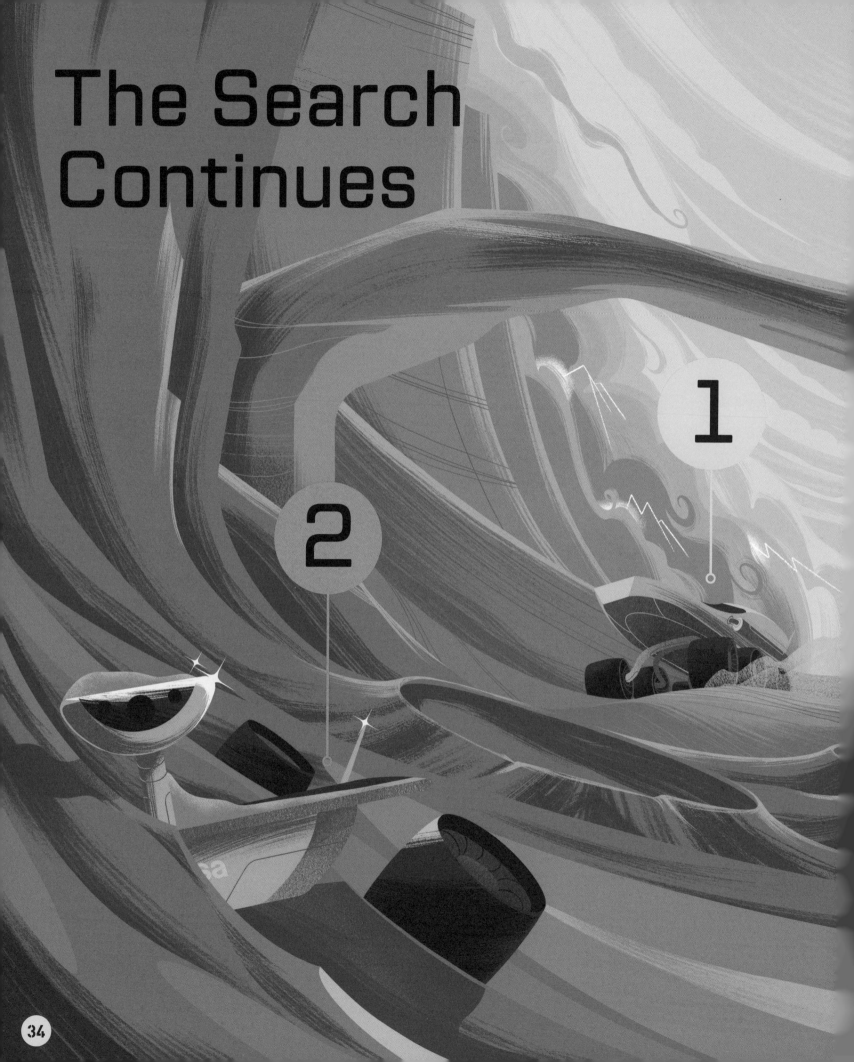

With the stress of the missing supplies bearing down on you, you start to feel panicked as you continue your search. It feels somewhat frantic as you navigate the surface, wondering where on *Mars* these supplies could be. On the horizon you see a dust storm creating havoc behind you, and no trace of the supplies.

Suddenly, out of the corner of your eye, you spot something glinting in the near distance! Could it be...?

1 Stick with your planned route. **Turn to page 40**

2 Investigate the glinting object. **Turn to page 46**

Navigating on Foot

The initial decision is to set out on foot, but there are mixed opinions on whether or not this is a really bad idea. Is this the right choice? Your gut instinct feels confused. If you continue on foot, you might reach the supplies sooner, but the terrain is difficult for a rover, let alone a human on foot. The lower gravity makes walking feel strange, like walking through glue. You realise that in order to optimise your journey you need to walk half as slow as you normally would on Earth, and sometimes you should 'kangaroo jump' for optimum movement. Perhaps continuing in the ATV is a better choice? But the rover is cumbersome and clunky at times, and you don't want to lose sight of those life-saving supplies, especially not with a dust storm approaching. What should you do?

TRAINING LOG

Gravity on Mars is a third of the Earth's, so movement is slower. On Mars, you'd use less power to make yourself move, so you'd burn less energy which means you might be able to go on for longer. But the lower the gravity, the less traction you get, and to move in the best way you need to start leaping! This also means you touch the ground less, so there is less friction, and a lower forward force, so you essentially slow down!

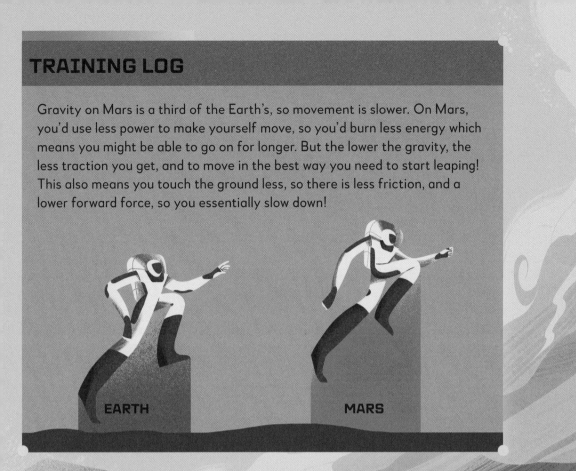

EARTH

MARS

The choice is yours...

1 Persist with walking. **Turn to page 38**

2 Return and collect the ATV. **Turn to page 32**

STA

91%
OXYGEN

DU

STO

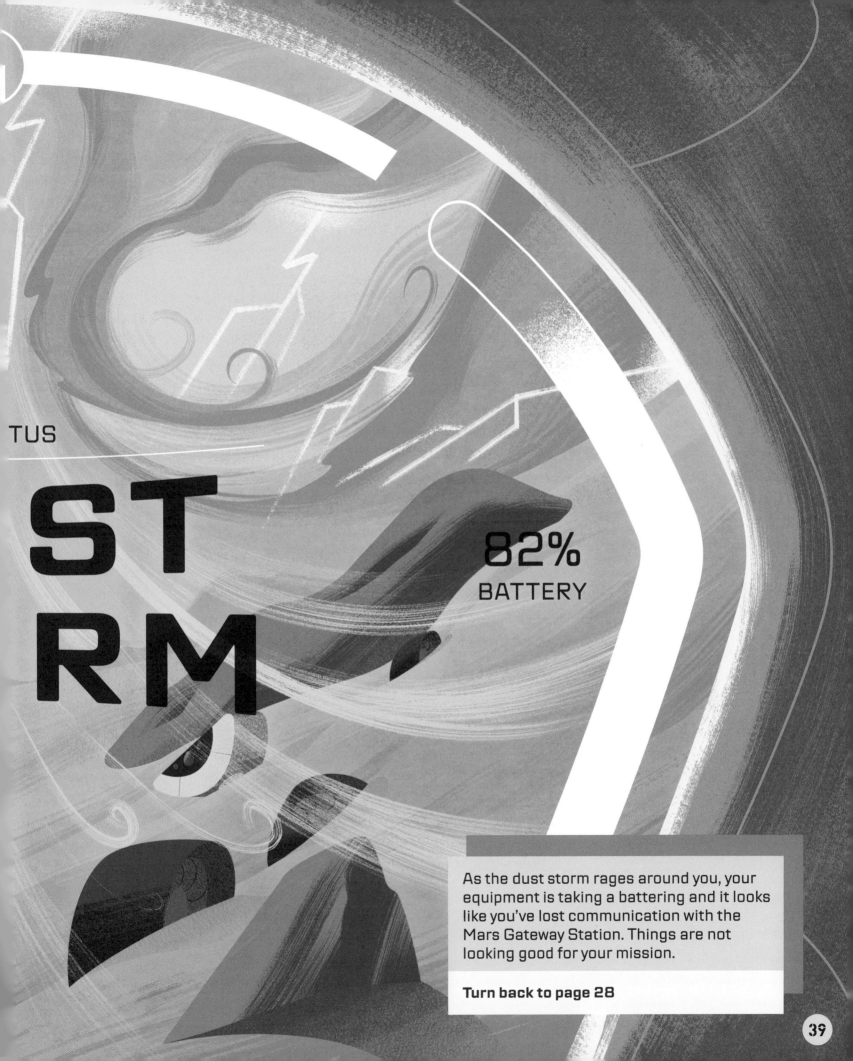

TUS

ST
RM

82%
BATTERY

As the dust storm rages around you, your equipment is taking a battering and it looks like you've lost communication with the Mars Gateway Station. Things are not looking good for your mission.

Turn back to page 28

Eberswalde Crater

There it is! Finally, you have reached the edge of the Eberswalde crater. Your gaze wanders around, scanning the landscape for your missing supplies. The crater is huge, dusty and wide. Part of the crater is buried, and part contains a river delta formation, suggesting that the crater could have once been a lake full of water. Buried under some sediment, you eventually spot the missing supplies. Relief floods your body, and you and the crew slowly make your way across the crater.

1

An impact crater on a planet or moon is formed when an object from space crashes into the surface. The object might be tiny, like a micrometeorite, or larger, like an asteroid, and it will have been travelling through space at thousands of kilometres when it collided with the planet. When a piece of space rock crashes into the solid surface at such incredible speeds, it smashes a crater into the terrain. The object becomes so hot it immediately vaporises, and the impact causes shock waves through the solid surface, melting the rock!

TRAINING LOG

There are 3 phases to making a crater;
contact, excavation and modification.

1. Contact is when an object hits the surface
and a shock wave is created.

2. Excavation is when the shock wave clears
the crater bed by throwing material about.

3. Modification is when the crater material falls back
into the crater. What's left behind is the big circular crater
hole, as well as some melted and resolidified rocks!

It's time to choose:

Respond to incoming message. **Turn to page 42**

2 Press on. **Turn to page 48**

41

Message from Base

Back on the station the control panel associated with the small Mars rovers starts to beep. This can only indicate one thing – there is a fault with one of the rovers! Without the rovers working properly, the crew can't collect their samples and the mission will fail! You frantically press buttons and keys, trying to work out the cause of the issue. You send a message to one of the satellites around Mars, instructing it to send photos of the rover in question.

ROVER4

The satellite is one of many circling Mars, helping the crew keep in contact with each other, and allowing communication between the surface and the station.

After what seems like forever, the images are downloaded to the control panel. Rover 4, the one closest to the crew back on the surface, has driven over a large rock and is now tipped over on its side! The rover isn't clever enough to right itself, you'll have to communicate with the crew on the surface to help.

Send the surface crew to investigate.

Turn to page 46

Investigate an Alarm

Suddenly, a blaring noise and red flashing lights start going off. There is a problem in the space station! The mission commander calmly leads the crew to a safe location and discusses the problem with the project engineer. The project engineer quickly checks the station's sensors. The sensors indicate that the oxygen levels are dropping. There must be a leak! The crew must work together in order to fix the problem and time is not on their side! The crew have to locate the leak and seal it before the oxygen levels in the station get dangerously low!

The project engineer uses the tech dashboard in the safe location to search the station for the location of the leak. They must stay calm and breathe normally, in order to solve the issue quickly and safely. Luckily, the project engineer knows the station inside out, and it doesn't take long to find the leak. The mission commander is able to lead the crew to fix the leak and everyone is once again safe to return to their jobs and get back to communicating with the crew on the surface.

With the danger over, it's time to relay the message to the surface crew.

To send the crew to the Ebserwalde crater. **Turn to page 40**

Rescue the Rover

A message is coming through the headset. The surface crew quieten down so that they are all able to hear the communication.

The crew discuss the options, then agree that they need to take a detour, and make their way to the rover so that the issue can be resolved. They're going to have to use some brute force to tip the rover back onto its wheels.

Gateway to surface crew! Come in surface!

Rover 4, I repeat, rover 4, has been overturned by a large looking object. The rover needs your assistance immediately, over.

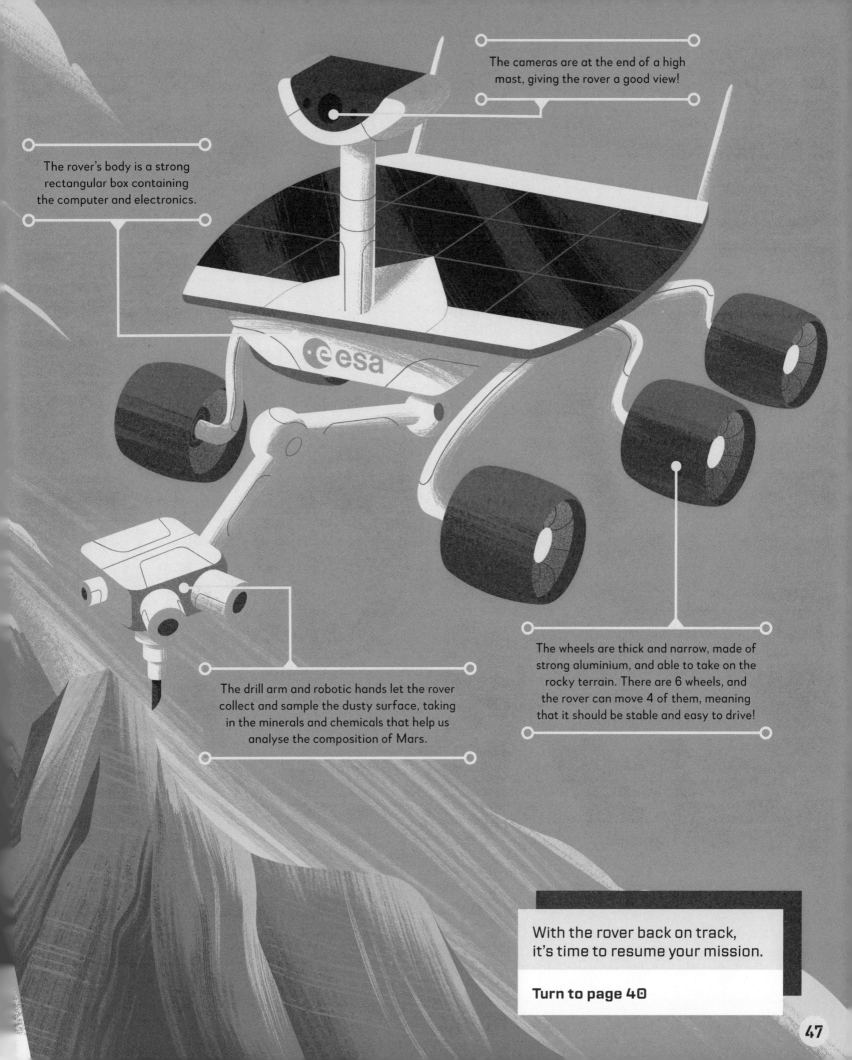

The cameras are at the end of a high mast, giving the rover a good view!

The rover's body is a strong rectangular box containing the computer and electronics.

The drill arm and robotic hands let the rover collect and sample the dusty surface, taking in the minerals and chemicals that help us analyse the composition of Mars.

The wheels are thick and narrow, made of strong aluminium, and able to take on the rocky terrain. There are 6 wheels, and the rover can move 4 of them, meaning that it should be stable and easy to drive!

With the rover back on track, it's time to resume your mission.

Turn to page 40

Collecting Samples

All your supplies and equipment are now accounted for and you and the crew can get back to doing what you do best – science! It is time to collect the samples. You are looking for Martian regolith; soil, rocks and dust. Once you are at the correct site, you will need to etch gently into the soil using the right tools, in order to collect multiple samples. Then you will have to pack them into sample tubes for safe keeping, ensuring no cross-contamination.

You have already brought some sample tubes from Earth so that when you do your analysis, you can compare what you find on Mars to a control sample from the home planet.

As the planetary protector you have the important, and legally required, role of ensuring that the sample collection is carried out safely, for the crew and the samples!

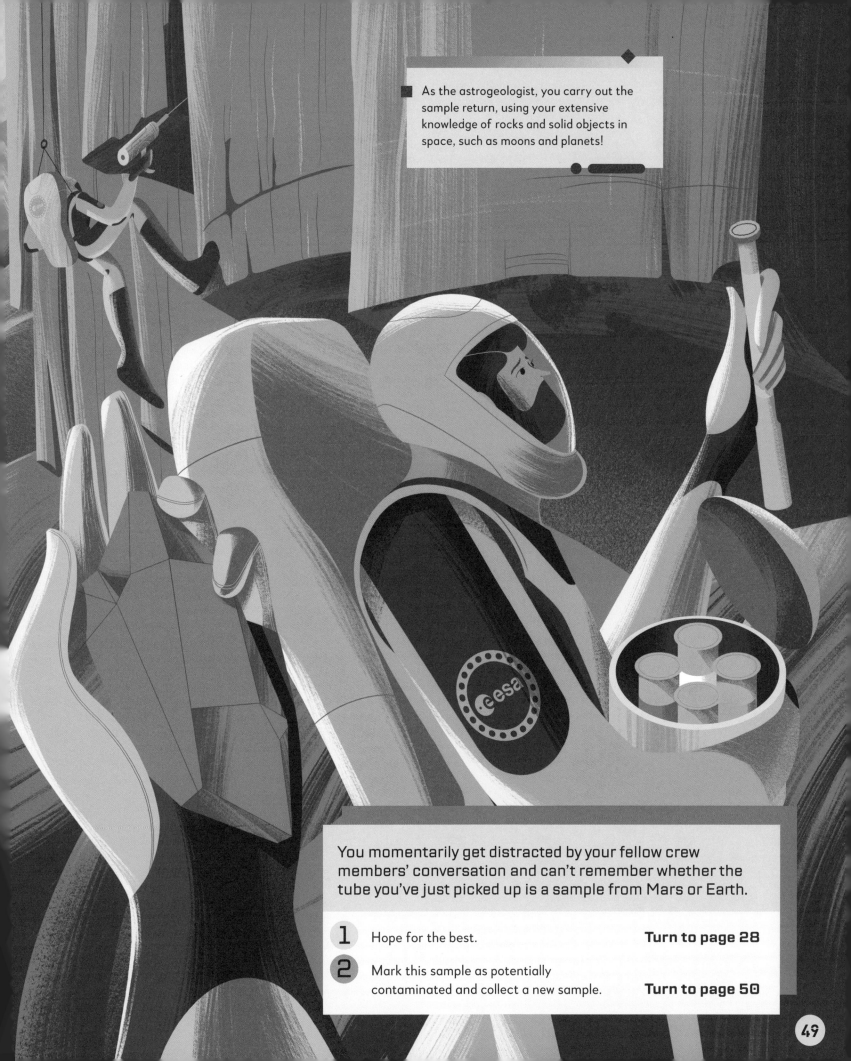

As the astrogeologist, you carry out the sample return, using your extensive knowledge of rocks and solid objects in space, such as moons and planets!

You momentarily get distracted by your fellow crew members' conversation and can't remember whether the tube you've just picked up is a sample from Mars or Earth.

1 Hope for the best. **Turn to page 28**

2 Mark this sample as potentially contaminated and collect a new sample. **Turn to page 50**

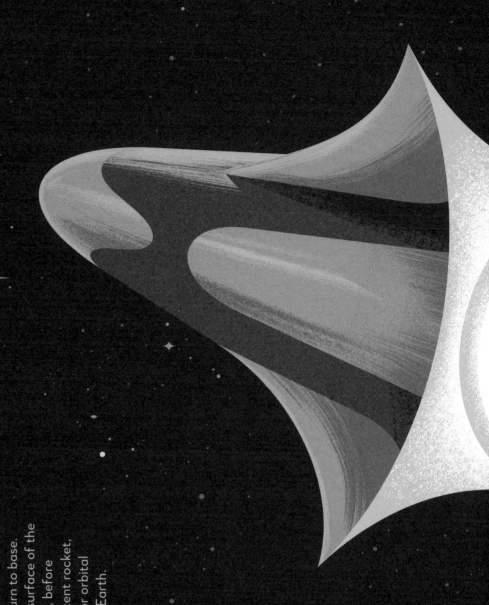

Ascend from the Surface of Mars

Your sample collection task has gone well, with all the tubes being filled safely and correctly. The capsules are sealed to make sure that the precious cargo remains intact. Now it is time to return to base. There, you will use the ascent rocket to launch off the surface of the red planet to return back to the Mars Gateway Station, before departing back to Earth to deliver the samples. The ascent rocket, with the crew and the samples inside, will rendezvous for orbital transfer, in preparation for eventually heading back to Earth.

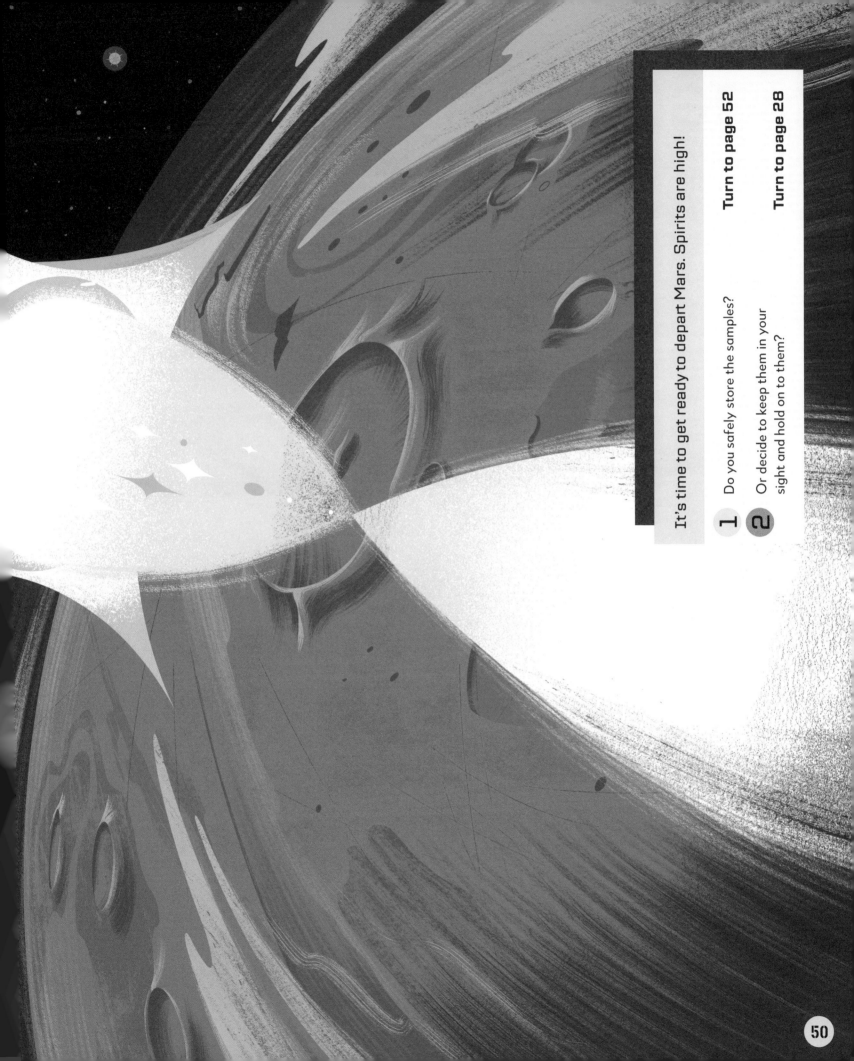

It's time to get ready to depart Mars. Spirits are high!

1 Do you safely store the samples?

Turn to page 52

2 Or decide to keep them in your sight and hold on to them?

Turn to page 28

Head Back to Earth

It's time for your final challenge – returning to Earth! You advise the crew on calculating the best orbit to use in order to arrive on Earth safely, using the re-entry systems and precision trajectories. This requires huge speeds; up to 50,000 km/h! Then you need to use Earth's atmosphere to slow you down so that you don't crash land into the blue planet, but you also don't want to be travelling so fast that your craft burns up in the atmosphere! There are so many challenges to get you home safely.

The spacecraft engine will decrease burn in order to start its re-entry into Earth's atmosphere. The atmosphere acts like a natural breaker, slowing the spacecraft down. This braking causes huge amounts of friction, which creates very high temperatures on the capsule but luckily it has thermal protection!

As the spacecraft slows down, the crew feel the G-force increase and are pushed back into their seats.

The crew have to ensure that they are wearing their special pressure suits for their rollercoaster final ride back home.

Just before landing, parachutes deploy to reduce the speed even more, and the spacecraft gently bumps down onto the surface of Earth.

Safely back on Earth, it is time to...

Turn to page 54

Initiate Landing

To find out if your mission was a success.

Turn to page 56

Mission Complete!

A few weeks later, after a brief period of rest and recuperation, you and some of your crew meet at the laboratory. The sample tubes filled with the Martian samples are ready and waiting for you to analyse. You each carry out your work on some of the samples, through observation and chemical testing. You are looking at texture, characteristics, smells, maybe even noises! Don't forget to wear your protective clothing and goggles.

You might add certain chemicals to the samples to see if a reaction occurs, watching for bubbling, listening for fizzing. Maybe gases are given off – you test to see if the gases are flammable.

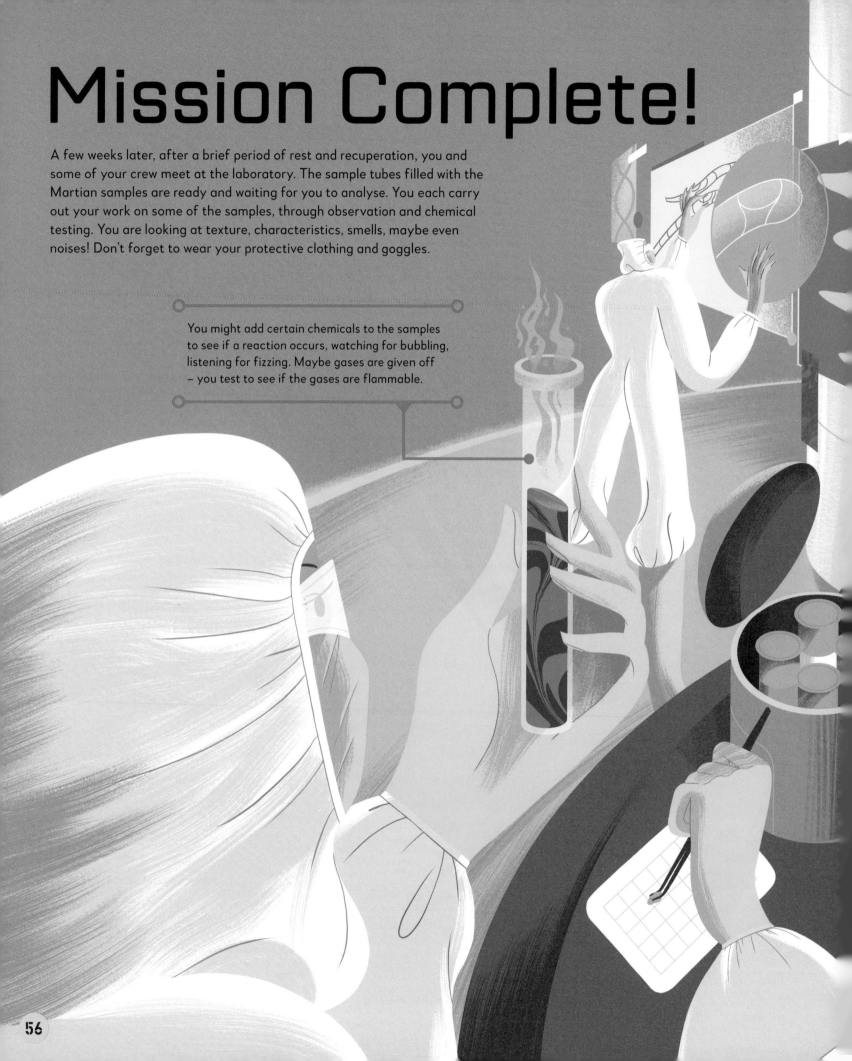

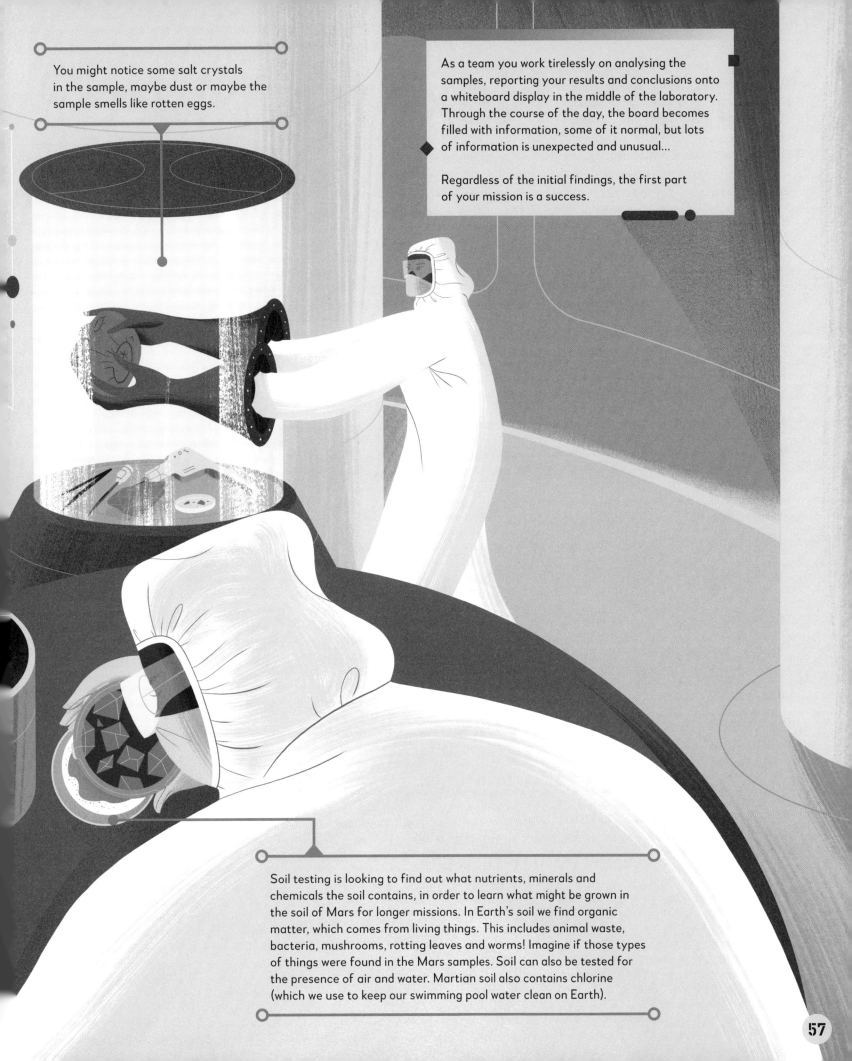

You might notice some salt crystals in the sample, maybe dust or maybe the sample smells like rotten eggs.

As a team you work tirelessly on analysing the samples, reporting your results and conclusions onto a whiteboard display in the middle of the laboratory. Through the course of the day, the board becomes filled with information, some of it normal, but lots of information is unexpected and unusual...

Regardless of the initial findings, the first part of your mission is a success.

Soil testing is looking to find out what nutrients, minerals and chemicals the soil contains, in order to learn what might be grown in the soil of Mars for longer missions. In Earth's soil we find organic matter, which comes from living things. This includes animal waste, bacteria, mushrooms, rotting leaves and worms! Imagine if those types of things were found in the Mars samples. Soil can also be tested for the presence of air and water. Martian soil also contains chlorine (which we use to keep our swimming pool water clean on Earth).

What's Next for Mars?

With the first mission to Mars ending successfully, with the sample return and testing of samples completed, what's next for you and your crew? The first trip didn't intend to leave anyone there, but eventually you will head up a crew who will know enough to be able to build a village on Mars. Next steps would be to visit again, explore a little more, find a water source, and work out a good location for a base. Another trip might transport a habitat and greenhouse to Mars, and test growing crops on the surface. There may be detours to Phobos and Deimos, or longer missions to the Mars Gateway. A final visit might be the one in which you plan to stay, for years, or perhaps, forever...

Glossary

Asteroid – A small rocky body that orbits the Sun.

Atmosphere – The layer of gas that surrounds the Earth.

Capsule - A spacecraft that can transport cargo, scientific experiments, and/or astronauts to and from space.

Contamination – The process of making something dirty, dangerous, or impure by adding something harmful or undesirable to it.

Crater – A bowl-shaped depression, or hollowed-out area on the surface of a planet.

Cupola – An observation area on a spacecraft.

Dashboard – A panel with dials and controls.

Deep space – Space beyond Earth's atmosphere.

Evolution – The gradual change over time.

Goldilocks Zone - The habitable zone around a star where it is not too hot and not too cold for liquid water to exist on the surface of surrounding planets.

Gravity – The force that pulls all objects in the universe towards each other.

Hazard – A risk or danger.

Microbial life – Tiny living things that are too small to see with the naked eye.

Module – A section of a spacecraft.

Orbit – The curved path taken by something moving round a planet or other body in space.

Orbiter – A vehicle that orbits a planet, moon, or other celestial body without landing on its surface.

Radiation – A form of energy that is emitted in rays, electromagnetic waves, and/or particles.

Satellite – A spacecraft sent into space to move in a orbit around a planet, in order to send and receive information.

Sediment – Solid matter that settles at the bottom of a liquid.

Solar array – A collection of solar panels that are wired together to capture sunlight and produce electricity.

Solar cells – A device that converts sunlight into electricity.

Solar flare – A giant explosion on the sun that releases a huge amount of energy in the form of radiation, light, and high-speed particles.

Terrain – Land or ground.

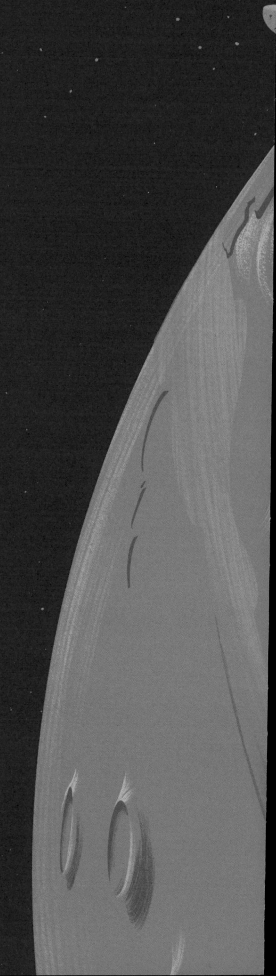

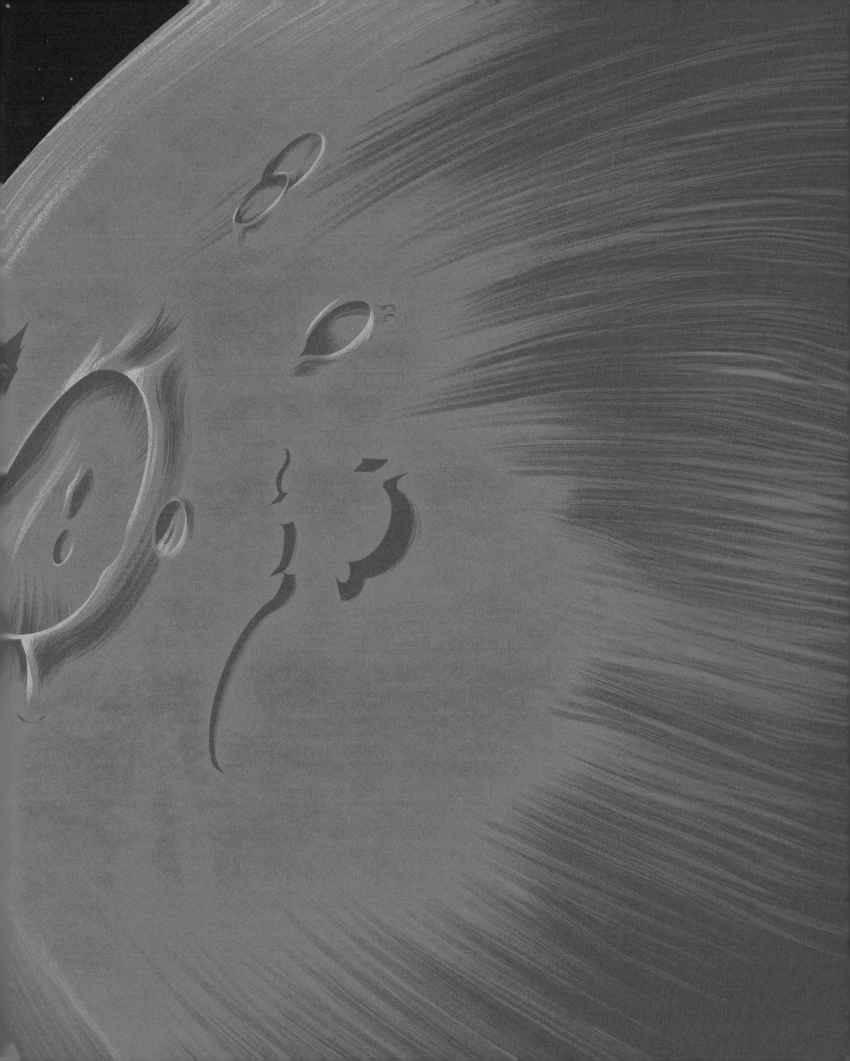

DK | Penguin Random House

Acquisitions Project Editor Sara Forster
Project Art Editor Stefan Georgiou
Senior Production Editor Jennifer Murray
Senior Production Controller Louise Minhane
Senior Acquisitions Editor Katy Flint
Design Manager Victoria Short
Managing Director Mark Searle

Designed for DK by Sarah Crookes
Text copyright © Dr Sheila Kanani, 2024
Illustrations by Adamastor Studio

DK would like to thank Charlie Donaldson and Alisha
Comber at Rocket Licensing; and Nadia Lueders and the
rest of the team at the ESA.

The European Space Agency is not a manufacturer or
distributor of the product. ESA authorised the branding of
the product with the ESA name, acronym, and/or logotype.
Licensed by Rocket Licensing on behalf of the ESA.

First published in Great Britain in 2024 by
Dorling Kindersley Limited
20 Vauxhall Bridge Road,
London SW1V 2SA

The authorised representative in the EEA is
Dorling Kindersley Verlag GmbH. Arnulfstr. 124,
80636 Munich, Germany

Copyright © 2024 Dorling Kindersley Limited
A Penguin Random House Company
10 9 8 7 6 5 4 3 2 1
001-342725-Nov/2024

A CIP catalogue record for this book
is available from the British Library.
ISBN: 978-02416-9333-9

Printed and bound in Slovakia

www.dk.com

MIX
Paper | Supporting
responsible forestry
FSC™ C018179

This book was made with Forest
Stewardship Council™ certified
paper – one small step in DK's
commitment to a sustainable future.
Learn more at **www.dk.com/uk/
information/sustainability**